# 100+ SOLOS *for* TRUMPET

*Wise Publications*
*London/New York/Paris/Sydney*

Exclusive Distributors:
Music Sales Limited
8/9 Frith Street,
London W1V 5TZ, England.

Music Sales Pty Limited
120 Rothschild Avenue,
Rosebery, NSW 2018,
Australia.

This book © Copyright 1992
by Wise Publications.
Order No.AM90026
ISBN 0-7119-3106-2

Cover design by Hutton Staniford.
Printed in the United Kingdom by
Caligraving Limited, Thetford, Norfolk.

Compiled by Peter Evans.
Music arranged by Steve Tayton.
Music processed by Upton & Skinner.

Instrument courtesy of Bill Lewington,
Shaftesbury Avenue, London WC2H 8NN.

Music Sales' complete catalogue lists
thousands of titles and is free from your
local music shop, or direct from
Music Sales Limited. Please send a
cheque/postal order for £1.50 for postage to:
Music Sales Limited, Newmarket Road,
Bury St. Edmunds, Suffolk IP33 3YB.

Your Guarantee of Quality

As publishers, we strive to produce every
book to the highest commercial standards.
The music has been freshly engraved and the
book has been carefully designed to minimise
awkward page turns and to make playing
from it a real pleasure.
    Particular care has been given to
specifying acid-free, neutral-sized paper
which has not been chlorine bleached but
produced with special regard for the
environment.
    Throughout, the printing and binding have
been planned to ensure a sturdy, attractive
publication which should give years of
enjoyment.
    If your copy fails to meet our high
standards, please inform us and we will
gladly replace it.

# The Girl From Ipanema
## (Garota De Ipanema)

Original Words by Vinicius De Moraes English Lyric by Norman Gimbel Music by Antonio Carlos Jobim

# Perdido

Music by Juan Tizol Words by Harry Lenk and Ervin Drake

# Wave

Words & Music by Antonio Carlos Jobim

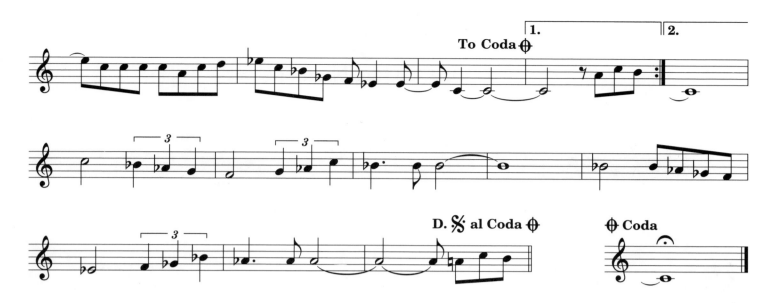

# Take The 'A' Train

*Words & Music by Billy Strayhorn*

# One Note Samba
# (Samba De Uma Nota So)

Original Words by N. Mendonca English Lyric by Jon Hendricks Music by Antonio Carlos Jobim

# Slightly Out Of Tune
## (Desafinado)

English Lyric by Jon Hendricks & Jessie Cavanaugh Music by Antonio Carlos Jobim

# That Ole Devil Called Love

Words & Music by Doris Fisher & Allan Roberts

# Take Five

By Paul Desmond

# Solitude

Words by Eddie de Lange & Irving Mills Music by Duke Ellington

# So Nice

Music & Original Lyrics by Marcos Valle & Paulo Sergio Valle English Lyrics by Norman Gimbel

**Music and lyrics by Alan Menken and Howard Ashman**

# THE LITTLE MERMAID

~ *"Under The Sea" from Walt Disney's "The Little Mermaid"* ~

1st B♭ Baritone

*Arranged by Frank Bernaerts*

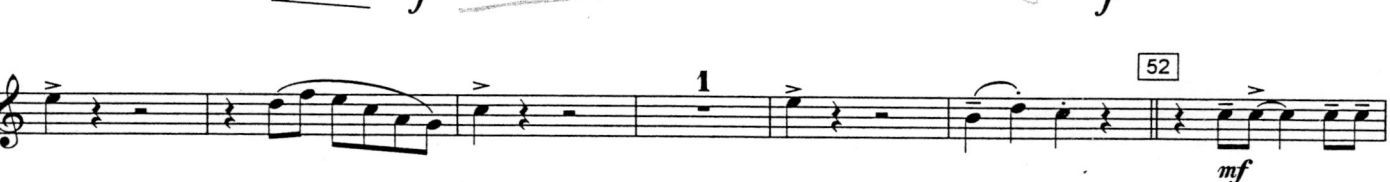

2001.0271

The main theme "Gabriels Oboe" from the motion picture

# THE MISSION

## BON-ACCORD SILVER BAND

Ennio Morricone,
*arranged by Frank Bernaerts*

**1st Bb baritone**

982

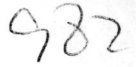

"A WHOLE NEW WORLD" from Walt Disney's motion picture

# ALADDIN

**1st Bb baritone**

Alan Menken,
*arr. Frank Bernaerts*

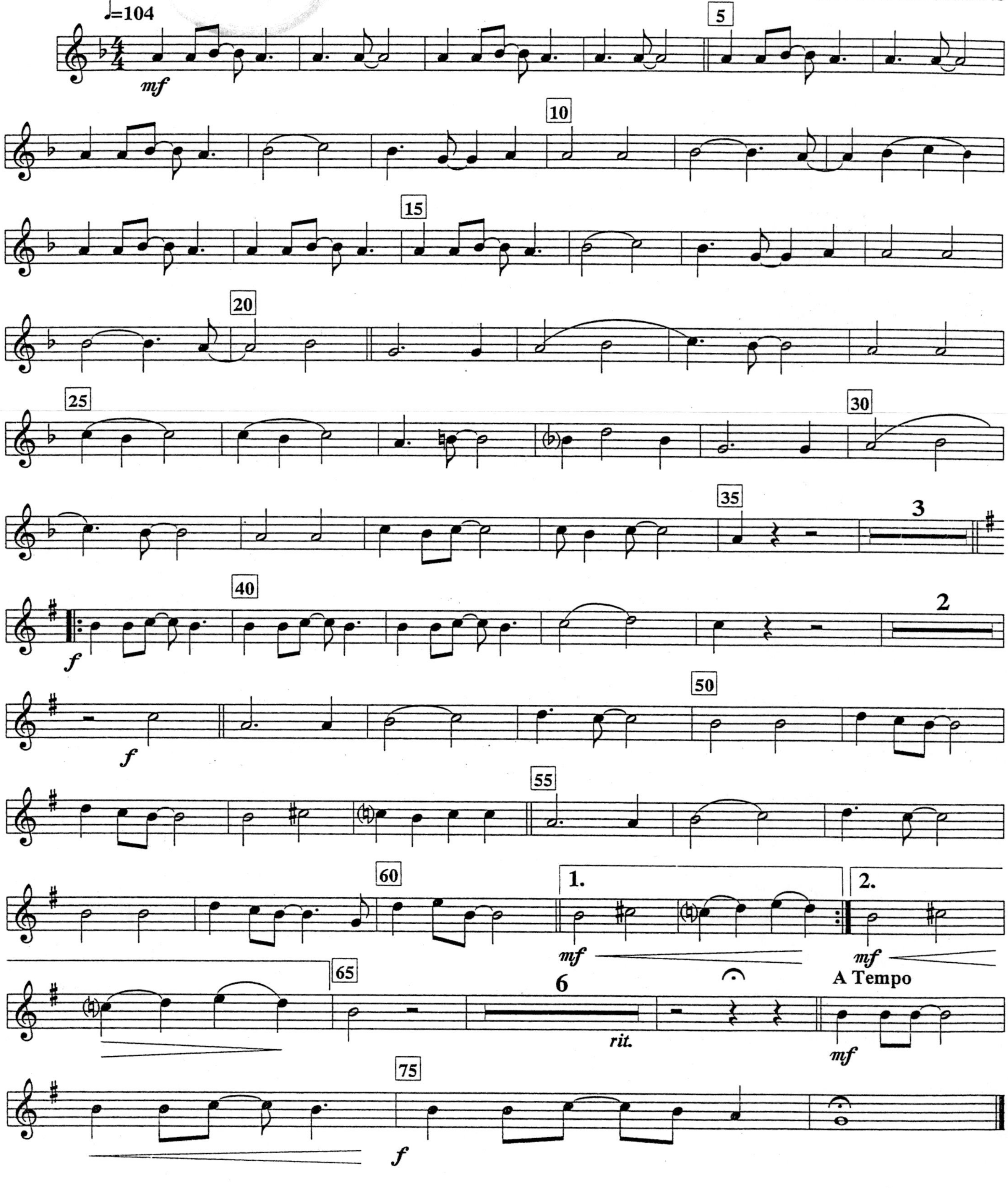

Arranged for Brass Band by
GOFF RICHARDS

Music by
ANDREW LLOYD WEBBER

**1st Bb BARITONE**

Tempo Commodo (Around ♩=112)

1st Bb Baritone

# JUBILATION!
## Fantasy on American spirituals

James Curnow

Recording on / Opname op / Enregistrement sur / Aufnahme auf:CD FIREWORK

920369

# No Matter What

**from Whistle Down The Wind**

Music by Andrew Lloyd Webber
arr. Ray Farr

1st Bb Baritone

6

# ANDANTE AND SCHERZO

Euphonium Solo with pianoforte accompaniment

REGINALD HEATH

PIANO
Andante

Andante cantabile,
con molto espress.

© 1969 R. SMITH & CO. LTD.

# ANDANTE
# AND SCHERZO

Euphonium Solo with pianoforte accompaniment

REGINALD HEATH

R. SMITH & CO. LTD.,

# It Came Upon the Midnight Clear

Trumpet II - Harmony

# I'm Beginning To See The Light

Words & Music by Harry James, Duke Ellington, Johnny Hodges & Don George

**Medium bounce**

# Round Midnight

Words & Music by Cootie Williams & Thelonious Monk

# Lullaby of Birdland

Music by George Shearing Words by George David Weiss

# Satin Doll

Words by Johnny Mercer Music by Duke Ellington & Billy Strayhorn

# All The Things You Are

Music by Jerome Kern Words by Oscar Hammerstein II

# It Don't Mean A Thing
## (If It Ain't Got That Swing)

Words by Irving Mills Music by Duke Ellington

# Luck Be A Lady

Words & Music by Frank Loesser

# I Believe In You

Words & Music by Frank Loesser

# If My Friends Could See Me Now

Words by Dorothy Fields Music by Cy Coleman

# Smoke Gets In Your Eyes

Music by Jerome Kern Words by Otto Harbach

# Can't Help Lovin' Dat Man

Music by Jerome Kern Words by Oscar Hammerstein II

# Woman

Words & Music by John Lennon

# Standing On The Corner

Words & Music by Frank Loesser

# I'll Never Fall In Love Again

Words by Hal David Music by Burt Bacharach

# Ol' Man River

Music by Jerome Kern Words by Oscar Hammerstein II

# I Know Him So Well

Words & Music by Benny Andersson, Tim Rice & Bjorn Ulvaeus

# Till There Was You

*Words & Music by Meredith Willson*

# I Dreamed A Dream
## (From The Musical 'Les Misérables')

Music by Claude-Michel Schonberg Lyrics by Herbert Kretzmer Original Text by Alain Boublil & Jean-Marc Natel

**Andante** (♩=72)

# Tonight

Music by Leonard Bernstein Lyrics by Stephen Sondheim

# So Amazing

Words & Music by Luther Vandross

**Repeat to fade**

# Seventy Six Trombones

Words & Music by Meredith Willson

# Sit Down, You're Rocking The Boat

Words & Music by Frank Loesser

# My Kind Of Girl

Words & Music by Leslie Bricusse

# Send In The Clowns

Words & Music by Stephen Sondheim

# I Don't Know How To Love Him

Music by Andrew Lloyd Webber Lyrics by Tim Rice

# Nobody Does It Better

Words by Carole Bayer Sager Music by Marvin Hamlisch

# Until It's Time For You To Go

Words & Music by Buffy Sainte-Marie

# Don't Cry For Me Argentina

Music by Andrew Lloyd Webber Lyrics by Tim Rice

# The First Time Ever I Saw Your Face

Words & Music by Ewan MacColl

# O For The Wings Of A Dove

Composed by Felix Mendelssohn

# Toreador's Song
## (from 'Carmen')

Composed by Georges Bizet

# La Donna È Mobile

Composed by Giuseppe Verdi

# Fourth Movement Theme
## ('From The New World')

Composed by Antonin Dvořák

# Land Of Hope & Glory
## (Pomp & Circumstance March)

Composed by Sir Edward Elgar

# Jerusalem

Music by Hubert Parry  Words by William Blake

# Theme From Swan Lake

Composed by Peter Ilyich Tchaikovsky

# You've Got A Friend

*Words & Music by Carole King*

# Your Song

Words & Music by Elton John and Bernie Taupin

# Jupiter
## (from 'The Planets Suite')

Composed by Gustav Holst

# To All The Girls I've Loved Before

Words & Music by Hal David & Albert Hammond

# This Guy's In Love With You

Words by Hal David Music by Burt Bacharach

# Truly

Words & Music by Lionel Richie

# When You're In Love With A Beautiful Woman

*Words & Music by Even Stevens*

# Wonderful Tonight

Words & Music by Eric Clapton

# Try A Little Tenderness

Words & Music by Harry Woods, Jimmy Campbell & Reg Connelly

**Slowly with expression**

# The Wind Beneath My Wings

Words & Music by Jeff Silbar & Larry Henley

# Unchained Melody

Music by Alex North Words by Hy Zaret

# The Lady In Red

Words & Music by Chris De Burgh

# On A Slow Boat To China

Words & Music by Frank Loesser

# The Power Of Love

Words & Music by C.deRouge, G.Mende, J.Rush & S.Applegate

# Caravan

By Duke Ellington, Irving Mills & Juan Tizol

# A Night In Tunisia

Music by Frank Paparelli & John 'Dizzy' Gillespie Words by Raymond Leveen

# Till Then

Words & Music by Guy Wood, Eddie Seller & Sol Marcus

# Blue Rondo A La Turk

By Dave Brubeck

# These Foolish Things

Words by Eric Maschwitz Music by Jack Strachey

# The Very Thought Of You

Words & Music by Ray Noble

# Strangers In The Night

Words by Charles Singleton & Eddie Snyder Music by Bert Kaempfert

# There I've Said It Again

Words & Music by Redd Evans & Dave Mann

# More Than I Can Say

Words & Music by Sonny Curtis & Jerry Allison

# September Morn

Words & Music by Neil Diamond & Gilbert Becaud

# The Mighty Quinn

Words & Music by Bob Dylan

**Moderately slow with a steady beat**

# Funny How Time Slips Away

Words & Music by Willie Nelson

# It's Impossible
# (Somos Novios)

Words by Sid Wayne Music by A. Manzanero

# Somewhere

Music by Leonard Bernstein Lyrics by Stephen Sondheim

# Love's Roundabout
## (La Ronde De L'Amour)

*French Words by Louis Ducreux English Words by Harold Purcell Music by Oscar Straus*

**Tempo di valsa**

# If You Leave Me Now

*Words & Music by Peter Cetera*

# An Old Fashioned Love Song

Words & Music by Paul Williams

# Bye Bye Love

Words & Music by Felice & Boudleaux Bryant

# Against All Odds
# (Take A Look At Me Now)

Words & Music by Phil Collins

# Just Like A Woman

Words & Music by Bob Dylan

# I'll Be Your Baby Tonight

Words & Music by Bob Dylan

# Something's Gotten Hold Of My Heart

Words & Music by Roger Cook & Roger Greenaway

# It's Over

Words & Music by Roy Orbison & Bill Dees

# How Deep Is Your Love

Words & Music by Barry Gibb, Robin Gibb & Maurice Gibb

# We Don't Talk Anymore

Words & Music by Alan Tarney

# As Time Goes By

Words & Music by Herman Hupfeld

# I'm Stone In Love With You

Words & Music by T. Bell, L. Creed & A. Bell

# If Not For You

Words & Music by Bob Dylan

# Moondance

Words & Music by Van Morrison

# Missing You

Words & Music by Chris De Burgh

# Let's Put It All Together

Words & Music by Hugo Peretti, Luigi Creatore, & George David Weiss

# Crazy

Words & Music by Willie Nelson

# Blowin' In The Wind

Words & Music by Bob Dylan

# Love Is Blue
## (L'Amour Est Bleu)

Music by André Popp Original Words by Pierre Cour English Lyric by Bryan Blackburn

# Softly Whispering I Love You

Words & Music by Roger Cook & Roger Greenaway

# Lay, Lady, Lay

Words & Music by Bob Dylan

# Feel Like Making Love

Words & Music by Eugene McDaniels

# Memories Are Made Of This

Words & Music by Terry Gilkyson, Richard Dehr & Frank Miller

# Forever Young

*Words & Music by Bob Dylan*

# Right Here Waiting

Words & Music by Richard Marx

# Endless Love

Words & Music by Lionel Richie

4/00 (37042)